New Optical Illusions

THIS IS A CARLTON BOOK

Text and artwork copyright © 2005 Archimedes' Laboratory Ltd
Design copyright © 2005 Carlton Books Ltd

First published in 2005 by Carlton Books Limited
20 Mortimer Street
London W1V 3JW

A CIP catalogue record for this book is available from the British Library

Senior Executive Editor: Roland Hall
Art Direction: Clare Baggaley
Design: Adam Wright
Production: Claire Hayward

ISBN 1 84442 327 1

Printed in Dubai

DEDICATION
For Antoinette Troïsi, my mother… who sometimes gives me the ILLUSION that the entire solar system rotates around me!
– G. Sarcone

PICTURE CREDITS
The authors would like to acknowledge the following sources. Any oversights, omissions or corrections will be updated in future editions of this work.

Pages 41, 108: Apparent rotations and Peripheral drift illusion based on research by J. Flaubert and A. Herbert.
Page 51: Peculiar cubic network based on Escher cubic space division illusion.
Page 101: Simultaneous brightness contrast based on Adelson checker-shadow illusion.
Page 102: Ghost triangle based on Kanisza triangle illusion.

Page 1: Where'd she come from?
The image is only composed of yellow, gray and green dots but if you look at it from a certain distance, the lovely face of Marilyn Monroe will appear, and the color of the complexion get a flesh-colored tint… even though there's no red or orange in the picture!

Page 3: Which color are the squares in the background?
The squares in the background could have two colors. Their color depends primarily on how we interpret the foreground objects: as a tilted series of multicolored squares, or as a grid?

New Optical Illusions

Over 150 Deceptive Images and Brain-Fooling Illustrations

Gianni Sarcone & Marie-Jo Waeber

CARLTON
BOOKS

Contents

'The organizational mechanisms of vision are best demonstrated by illusions. Illusions illustrate that perception is a creative construction that the brain makes in interpreting visual data... Learning does not prevent us from being taken in by these illusions'

– Eric Kandel, *Principles of Neural Science*.

INTRODUCTION

What you see isn't always what you get!

'The universe is full of magical things, patiently waiting for our wits to grow sharper', said Eden Phillpotts. Two of these magical things are so close to our nose we often just take them for granted:. we call them "eyes". Yes, we take vision for granted; that's why optical illusions are important, because they reveal the magic and the limits of our visual perception.

In the word "illusion" we find the Latin root *ludus*, which means "play". As illusions really play with our senses, they capture our attention and strike us as strange and interesting. So could it be that we are fascinated by optical illusions because we like to be mystified?

Growing literature on illusions reflects this popular interest and points to the fact that these sensations are not only interesting in themselves but are also sources for gaining insight into normal vision. Vision isn't quite a 100 per cent natural process as folk may think. It depends to a large extent on learned skills that are helpful in interpreting the real world, but can sometimes deceive. People in the most remote and isolated parts of the world, who have never seen photographs, cannot at first understand what a photograph depicts when it is shown to them. The interpretation of this particular kind of visual representation is a learned skill.

What actually are optical or visual illusions? In the fewest words, they are particular illusions that deceive the human visual system into perceiving something that is not present or incorrectly perceiving what is present. There are two kinds of optical illusions: physiological illusions and cognitive illusions. Physiological illusions are the effects on the eyes or brain of prolonged stimulation of a specific type: brightness, tilt, color, movement. Cognitive illusions interact with different levels of perceptual processing and in-built assumptions or "knowledge" are misdirected. Cognitive illusions are commonly divided into ambiguous illusions, distorting illusions, paradox illusions, or fiction illusions.

Optical illusions have been studied for millenia. Even our prehistoric ancestors may have been puzzled by visual illusions, although they didn't leave traces of it. They must surely have noticed and experienced some visual phenomena such as: the after-image effect on their eyes, when looking into the sun; a stick that seems broken when half of it is put in water; the Moon illusion (the rising Moon seems twice as large as the Moon in its zenith); and the natural optical phenomenon called a mirage.

The ancient Greeks used a technique known as *entasis* which incorporates a slight convexity in the columns of the Parthenon to compensate for the illusion of concavity created by parallel lines.

In English, there are two essential words to express the faculty and the act of seeing: "see" and "view". The etymological sense of the words "see" and "view" are "follow something with the eyes" (from the Indo-European *seq*) and "have learned" (from the Indo-European *weid*). So, for our ancestors, an image was something to shape with the eyes (follow with the eye) and information taken from the real world (having learned from this visual perception).

Just gray...

Color experiment with gray lines... What happens is called color assimilation: the gray color appears bluish in contact with blue, and orange-colored in contact with orange, giving the impression of a color gradation.

Unfortunately (or fortunately?), seeing isn't some kind of direct perception of reality. Atcually, our bairns are cnostanlty itnerperting, corrceting and gviing srtuctrues to the viusal ipnut form our eeys (see footnote below). If this were not the case, we wouldn't see any colors, and we would probably see the world upside down! We would also notice in our visual field a very large dot, called the blind spot, where the optic nerve enters the eye. Another interesting everyday paradox of our vision is that we don't see the edges of our visual field! In fact, we should see black zones outside of our visual field, but our brains cancel out these zones with a smooth fade-out effect.

To resume, optical illusions teach us how we perceive things. But beyond the scientific aspect, they are great fun to look at. They can intrigue and entertain us. In this book, you will find a unique collection of visual puzzles to solve and optical illusions to explore, to enjoy and to experiment with. In this book there are seven main types of illusion: ambiguous figures, impossible figures, hidden figures, color perception, moving patterns, paradoxes and magic. This last topic includes true logic and visual paradoxes together with some neat mind bamboozlement. A large part of the illusions contained in this book were invented and designed by the authors, some others are adaptations of lesser-known optical illusions or based on recent studies made by leading researchers in the field of the cognitive neurosciences, such as E. Andelson, H. Ashida, J. Faubert, G. Kanisza, A. Kitaoka, A. Logvinenko, B. Pinna and H. Van Tuijl.

Each illusion, when necessary, is explained with simple and clear words – this book is intended for everyone – but please be aware that most of the explanations are empirical and based on intuition rather than on real scientific proof. Some perceptive illusions are still under discussion and the scientists who studied these phenomena are only able to make suppositions. The best way to understand how and why an illusion works is to experience it with your friends and try constructing a variant. If the variant works, that means that you have understood the secret mechanism of the illusion. This book is a large compendium of new and interesting illusions and we hope that you will use our stunning illustrations as a resource and inspiration for designing and creating new optical illusions.

Most probably your brain has automatically corrected the sentence to, 'Actually, our brains are constantly interpreting, correcting and giving structure to the visual input from our eyes.' It's amazing, isn't it?

'This shoe fits like a glove'
– Yogi Berra.

Tight position
Are you really looking at this man reading from behind? This is a kind of undecidable figure. The lower and upper part of the man seem to have different directions.

Figure it out (ambiguous and completion figures)

Does the mind represent the world accurately and unambiguously? Actually, ALL inputs to the brain are, to one degree or another, "ambiguous", allowing multiple interpretations. That's the reason why we have poets, artists, singers. The capacity to perceive and give different meanings to our environment is part of our human condition.

The most famous example of ambiguity in painting is the smile of the Mona Lisa by Leonardo da Vinci. In his book *The Story of Art*, Ernest Gombrich reports: 'Even in photographs of the painting we experience this strange effect, but in front of the original in the Paris Louvre it is almost uncanny. Sometimes she seems to mock at us, and then again we seem to catch something like sadness in her smile.' Ambiguous figures, also known as equivocal images or metamorphic images, are of special interest in the investigation of thinking. This is because they exemplify the fact that sometimes the same perceptual input can lead to very different representations, suggesting that the brain is actively involved in interpreting what we see rather than passively recording it. The curious aspect of ambiguous figures is that once you have perceived both figures, it is impossible to focus on only one without the other popping into your vision from time to time. Our brain, in fact, resolves visual ambiguity by means of oscillation.

Ambiguous figures include figure-ground illusions, ambigrams and what we will call completion figures. Figure-ground illusions are illusions that swap around the main figure and its background. Ambigrams are graphic words or sentences that can be read in more than one way. Completion figures are patterns which the mind rather unambiguously interprets in a particular way despite the fact that the input is incomplete in relation to what is typically "perceived".

A certain style of completion figure, called droodles, was used in the late 1950s to entertain puzzle enthusiasts and magazine readers. These cartoons were rather abstract line drawings accompanied by an implicit question: 'what is it?' A punchline (usually a funny description) finally made the cartoons obvious. Completion figures and droodles are based on *pareidolia* (payr-eye-DOH-lee-uh), an innate human tendency to impose a pattern on random or ambiguous shapes. Astronomer Carl Sagan claimed that this tendency to see faces in tortillas, clouds, cinnamon buns, and the like is an evolutionary trait. He writes: 'As soon as the infant can see, it recognizes faces, and we now know that this skill is hardwired in our brains. Those infants who a million years ago were unable to recognize a face smiled back less, were less likely to win the hearts of their parents, and less likely to prosper. These days, nearly every infant is quick to identify a human face and to respond with a goony grin.' (Sagan, 1995.)

Giving meaning to abstract forms can also be a way to exercise our visual thinking skills. Even da Vinci heartily recommended this method of invention as a practical technique for "opening the mind and putting it upon the scent of new thoughts". He once wrote: 'If you look upon an old wall covered with dirt or the

Brighten it up

The colors of the rainbow in A are faded. To restore their intensity, stare at the white dot in figure B for 20–30 seconds, then shift your gaze back to figure A. This effect is based on color adaptation.

odd appearance of some streaked stones, you may discover several things like landscapes, battles, clouds, uncommon attitudes, humorous faces, draperies...'

'A knife without a blade for which the handle is missing'

– G. C. Lichtenberg, in Göttingen Pocket Calendar.

THAT'S IMPOSSIBLE (impossible figures)

When we observe a two-dimensional picture on paper, we often interpret it as a three-dimensional figure. This insistence on viewing objects as three-dimensional can lead to interesting perceptual problems.

An impossible object, also called an undecidable figure, is an object that cannot exist according to the known laws of physics but has a description or representation suggesting, at first sight, that it can be constructed. Generally, impossible objects depend on the ambiguous connectivity possible in line drawings. We like to call these improbable objects Frankenstein figures because they are made by matching together two or more different points of view of the same object, or by extending and blending together the perspective of one object with another one. Some impossible figures are not immediately obvious: you have to focus your attention on a particular zone of the representation of

the object – the line of fusion of the contrasting perspectives – to understand that it cannot be realized. The paradox is that if you consider a sufficiently small zone of the drawing, the oddness disappears. That is to say, the "impossibility" is not here, or there – it is something about the object as a whole. This paradox could perfectly illustrate the philosophical principle which says that, "The whole is something completely different from the sum of its parts."

The more the impossible object looks normal, the more it is fascinating! Impossible figures aren't created to baffle your eyes; their structure should appear coherent and logical. They are designed to confuse your mind. The "undecidability" of these figures invariably rests on them being interpreted as two-dimensional projections of what would be an impossible higher-dimensional object. Artist Maurice Escher is notable for many drawings that feature undecidable figures, sometimes the entire drawing being an impossible figure. Oscar Reutersvärd, another important artist, has conducted a lifelong exploration into the world of impossible figures, producing a prodigious body of work during his long career.

Notable modern undecidable figures include:

– impossible cube;
– Penrose stairs;
– Penrose triangle;
– blivet (or Devil's Pitchfork).

We should not forget to add Mickey Mouse's ears to the list. Yes, his ears do not follow the basic rules of perspective.

Quick color eyesight test

Close one eye and stare at the two colored squares each containing the letter E. If one of the E's seems darker you may need a pair of glasses! Do the test with the other eye too. This test is based on the chromatic aberration of the lens in our eye making red colors focus slightly behind the retina and green colors, slightly in front. In normal conditions chromatic aberration passes unnoticed, but a slight nearsightedness or farsightedness increases the irregularity making a color go over the edges of a letter E.

Children and adults alike are so accustomed to the current aspect of this cartoon character that they don't notice at all that his ears are actually impossible figures! But impossible figures have a long history. In 1025, an unknown European artist unintentionally drew the first example of impossible figure art (three impossible pillars), in a painting *Madonna a Gyermekkel* ("Madonna and Child – Adoration of the Magi"). Another example of an impossible artistic object (a gallows!) was painted by Pieter Brueghel in *Magpie on the Gallows* (1568). However, the first artist who "deliberately" misuses perspective to create an absurd and impossible landscape is the famous English artist William Hogarth (1697-1764) whose artwork *Perspective Absurdities* formed the frontispiece to J. J. Kirby's book *Dr Brook Taylor's Method of Perspective Made Easy in Both Theory and Practice* (1754). This book was intended to teach people how to draw in perspective, so the caption asserted: 'Whoever makes a design without the knowledge of perspective will be liable to such absurdities as are shown in this frontispiece.'

'Three things cannot be long hidden: the sun, the moon, and the truth'

– Gautama Siddharta, the founder of Buddhism.

FIND THE OBJECT (hidden objects)

In France, prints called *images d'Épinal* were given to children by grocers as a premium gift. These cards depicted traditional scenes of everyday life, historical facts, legends or visual riddles, and were popular in the latter half of the 1800s and in the early 1900s. The object of these puzzling cards was often to find a hidden image (or several hidden images) within a picture. At that time, children delighted when they found the latent image hidden in the manifest image. This innocent mental process is related to the concept of the lost object used in psychoanalysis. Finding the object "is just a process of retrieving something that is already there," asserted Freud.

Since then, hidden-figure puzzles have been appreciated worldwide by puzzle enthusiasts. The principle is still the same. A hidden-figure puzzle is mostly a single image accompanied by a caption below it. The text, one or two lines long, introduces the image and indicates the object to be found in the drawing: an animal, a human being, a geometric shape and so on. The image should then be turned in every direction to find the hiding-place of the subject.

Basically, hidden image puzzles are also optical illusions because they bring into play the foreground and background relationships of our visual perception. The term pregnance (from the German word "Prägnanz") is applied in psychology to the tendency to distinguish certain objects from their background. Some shapes, like discs, have the property of being more easily detected than other ones, even when they are incomplete or

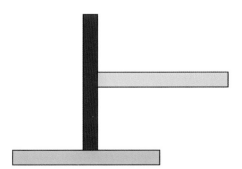

Yellow rod = green rod?
The rods form the Chinese character 'high'. Are the yellow and green rods of the same length? They are – measure them!

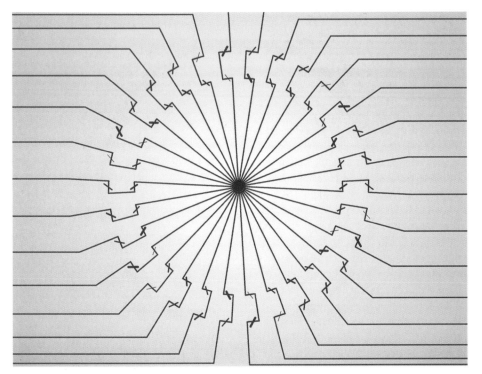

Follow my eyes

Stare at the center of the geometric picture shown here A. Keeping your gaze fixed on the central blue spot, move your head backwards and forwards several times. What happens? The blue concentric circles appear to rotate in opposite directions!

Photocopy the optical illusion and paste it on a rectangular piece of cardboard. Then, keeping the image 30cm away from your eyes, repeat the swinging movements. What do you see now? The concentric circles seem to expand or shrink, like the aperture of a camera, depending on the swinging direction you give to the image.

surrounded by a large quantity of other forms. But this isn't as natural or evident as you may think, and this will be demonstrated by the tests you'll encounter on the following pages. Normally, your brain 'reads' your visual field like a book, trying to discriminate the meaningful letters (objects) from the meaningless page (background). This process of distinction is not always easy, as there are elements that can cause 'noise' which is the result of an over-abundance of images, misperception or deliberate camouflage and encryption. Hidden figures are widely used in neuropsychological tests to measure figure-ground discrimination. These tests are called Embedded Figures Tests (EFT). Why not do the tests on the following pages? You can do them alone or with your friends. The time allocated to resolve each picture is five minutes. Those who score highly are described as being field-independent, and have ability to "distinguish the message from the noise", while those who find it difficult to find the hidden shapes are called field-dependent and have a greater tendency to perceive complete patterns rather than their separate components.

The secret to solving hidden figures lies in losing yourself in the whole scene, and not in a particular area that seems at a first sight to have more probability of hiding the figure than another area. Don't act like the drunken man searching for his keys within the cone of light below a street-lamp, who answered a helpful passerby enquiring if he was sure that he had lost them within the cone of light: 'No, of course not; it's dark over there.'

'I often think that the night is more alive and more richly colored than the day'

— Vincent Van Gogh.

COLOR CO-ORDINATION? (color and brightness effects)

We have a secret we want to share with you. Color doesn't exist at all in nature! Color only starts to exist when our perception systems produce the impression of 'color'. Light is perceived on the retina as a stimulus and is processed into a perception of color in our brain. In substance, colors are already illusions in themselves. Color serves a special function in the processes of vision. Our ability to analyze and process colors is a result of having three types of cone receptors in the retina, which have different light wavelength sensitivities. Sure, the eye is not a perfect optical instrument due to possible chromatic aberration of the lens, yellowing with age, and variations of sensitivity. But, coupled with the brain, human vision is satisfactorily reliable and constant.In certain situations, some of the effects that the brain uses to enhance vision can be observed. These include after-image, assimilation, changing color sensibilities, chromatic aberration, retinal rivalry, retreating and advancing colors, lightness constancy, simultaneous contrast and the influence of color on apparent size and weight. Color adaptation or assimilation is

Continuous lines?
Are the oblique lines in the square continuous from side to side? No, but you have to take a closer look at the pattern in order to realize it.

Grey sofa
Is the gray zone in a) darker than the gray zone in b)? The gray zones in a) and b) have exactly the same hue. We tend to perceive the gray zone in a) to be darker. This experiment shows that the perceived brightness doesn't rely only on the amount of light that reaches the eye from the observed object.

the tendency of the eye to adapt in seconds to most prevailing light sources. Because of this effect, the eye can, in turn, accurately identify the colors of objects under changing lighting conditions. Adaptation will be seen by a person traveling in a vehicle with tinted windows; if, for instance, the tint is blue, the landscape will at first seem suffused with a blue cast, but as the eye quickly desensitizes itself to blue the view will soon reassume its normal coloration.

Lightness constancy: objects that are viewed under different lighting conditions usually "look" the same to us. For example, a white T-shirt will look the same whether it is brightly lit on a sunny day or dimly lit on an overcast day. This is despite the fact that the wavelength of light that reaches the retinas in each case is different. This is explained by the fact that the brightness of an object's surroundings usually change in proportion to the change in brightness of the object itself.

After-image is a negative or complementary 'ghost' of a color seen after prolonged stimulation of the eye. An after-image occurs by staring first at a black spot on a white surface for around 20 seconds; then, shifting one's gaze to a black surface, a floating white spot will be seen briefly. The after-image of a red spot would be blue-green, that of a blue one would be yellow-orange, and that of a violet spot would be greenish-yellow. After-image effects involve the optic nerves. An optical nerve is composed of millions of neuronal fibers which connect the retina to the brain by decoding the stimuli of the retina into three different signals: light difference (black/white) or luminance, red/green color difference and blue/yellow color difference. When you stare at a red square for 20 seconds and more, the cells of the optic nerve, those which transmit the presence of red AND the absence of green will be under tension and will be saturated; consequently, when the stimulus suddenly disappears, the brain will interpret this stimulus cut effectively as the absence of red AND the presence of green. A green square will therefore appear in your visual field. It's like a short flip-flop effect. Interestingly, most standards for television transmission use a very similar decoding system with one luminance and two chrominance channels. A curious effect called retinal rivalry may be obtained by stimulating both retinas, each with a different color. For instance, when a blue glass is placed before one eye and a yellow or red one before the other, the two independent monocular fields fight for supremacy; vision appears alternately in one color and then the other, and the brain has great trouble resolving the images. (This is not a problem associated with 3-D motion pictures!) Simultaneous color contrast is an effect in which the contrast between adjacent colors is enhanced by the eye. The effect is particularly strong with a pair of complementary colors, such as red and green or orange and blue. If these colors are put together in tight patterns, the resulting contrast is so strong that flicker will occur and the eye may experience considerable discomfort. Simultaneous lightness contrast is an effect in which a color of given brightness will look darker on a light background and brighter on a dark background. Simultaneous contrasts depend on lateral inhibition of our visual system. Some photoreceptors of the retina are activated when they detect light, while others are activated in the absence of light. These two types usually encircle each other and are spread throughout the retina, creating receptive fields. Often, light can fall on to both light and dark photoreceptors causing the two regions to compete with one another. One part of the receptive field wants to become active while the other part does not. This competitive interaction is called lateral inhibition. Because of this antagonistic nature of receptive fields, perceptual illusions, such as the Herman or Lingelbach grid illusion, can occur when we look at certain patterns containing contrasting colors. Since warm (reddish) colors tend to advance and cold (bluish) colors tend to recede in our visual field, objects painted in red and orange will seem to be slightly larger than those painted in the cool blues and greens. Red cars or buses may seem larger than they actually are, but a room painted in red will seem more confined than a blue one. The reason for these effects is chromatic aberration, a problem associated with lenses (including the one used to focus light in the human eye) in which light is refracted by different amounts according to its wavelength. As a result, yellow is the only color perfectly focused by the normal eye, with red focused slightly behind the retina and blue slightly in front. The second reason may be that associative elements come into play. For example, blue may seem to recede because of the association it has in our memory with distance (the sky, sea, distant mountains). The value (relative lightness or darkness) of a color also affects our perception of the weight of an object. In the following pages you will experience some effects related to color, including color and lightness illusions, neon color spreading effect, scintillating grid effect, Kanisza illusion, Boynton filling-in phenomenon...

'Things are not what they seem; nor are they otherwise'

— excerpt from Lankavatara Sutra.

IN THE MIND'S EYE
(length, size and shape misperception)

Our brain often translates the physical image we perceive into an image which is more useful to our senses. As you experience it in everyday life, there is a distinction between the actual size of an object, its apparent size and its imaginary size. The actual size of an object cannot be observed, because in order for our eyes to focus upon that object it must be at a certain distance. But you can calculate or measure it. The apparent size of an object depends on several factors described below. A camel may not pass through the eye of a needle, but its image – apparent size – can. Actually, it would be possible to see through a 2mm wide eye of a needle a 2m wide camel placed at a distance of 1km from you. What about the imaginary size? Psychologically, we tend to see objects larger (or smaller) than they appear in reality. For example, it's very difficult to determine at a rough guess the real size of circular objects.

The fact that we have two eyes (binocular vision) is more than sufficient to provide information on distances, and for that reason we don't need three. One of these binocular distance cues is called convergence. Convergence refers to the turning-in of our eyes as objects come closer to our eyes (and is what causes you to have a squint!). The other thing that happens as objects come closer is that our visual accommodation changes.

Another cue to distance perception, especially for more complex scenes in which there are multiple objects, is binocular disparity. That means that each eye records a different angle of the visual field. Yet another cue to distance is motion parallax. As you move from one location to another, objects at various distances will move in a direction dependent on where you are fixating. Finally, it turns out that color and brightness can also have an effect on how far away something appears.

The perceived or apparent size of objects depends primarily on the visual angle subtended by the object on the retina in our eyes. All other things being equal, the object that subtends the larger visual angle will appear larger. The visual angle is dependent on the real size of the object and on the distance the object is from our eyes.

Another factor affecting perceived size is size constancy. This phenomenon results in objects of known size tending to appear constant in size regardless of their actual distance. So, for example, if you are looking at your friend and that friend starts walking away from you, the friend does not, at the same time, start to appear smaller even though the visual angle subtended by that friend is getting less and less. Well, size constancy also depends on the distance, and if it is large enough, known objects will appear smaller. If you have ever looked at the ground from a very tall building, you will have noticed that people on the sidewalks and cars in the streets look very small indeed. Perspective also plays a part in perception of size.

In conclusion, despite our ability to judge distance and size differences in many cases, our ability is distorted by a wide range of subjective factors. What is really interesting is that size illusions affect only the visual

Temple of colors

Examine the pale purple rectangles on the Greek temple. Are they of the same shade? Or do some rectangles appear darker than other ones? The pale purple rectangles are all the same hue. Objects tend to be darker when placed on a clear luminous background and vice versa.

perception, but not the senses which control our organs of motion. Thus, scientists presume that there are two kinds of visual connections, one directly concerning visual perception and the other involving motory control.

Let's talk about illusions. If the mother of all illusions in size perception is the Müller-Lyer illusion – published in the prestigious journal *Archiv für Anatomie und Physiologie* in 1889 – the father is the Ponzo illusion. We can say that all modern illusions on size distortion are based on these two contributions. The Müller-Lyer and Ponzo illusions are clearly related to the effect of perspective. In the Müller-Lyer illusion, the fins and the arrows at both ends of the lines provide a sensation of receding and advancing corners; in the Ponzo illusion, the angle of the converging lines in the background creates apparent depth through linear perspective.

In this book we will explore some of the things that affect our ability to estimate comparative lengths, sizes, and shapes and examine some geometrical properties that induce those deformations. We will also take into consideration the so-called alignment illusions and perceptive distortions, whereby repeating regular background patterns can so strongly dominate other regular geometric shapes placed on to them that they appear distorted (not aligned or parallel, bulging or swelling).

'Eppur si muove!' (But it does move!)

– Galileo Galilei, according to legend, muttered this under his breath after being forced by the Inquisition to declare that the Earth always remains still.

MOVING PARTS (illusory moving patterns)

How is it possible to create the illusion of motion with geometric and static images? There is a branch of modern art named Op Art (short for "Optic art") which is concerned with such optic effects. Op Art paintings often play with optic interference and moiré to create illusory colors and motion. The precursor of the Op Art was Victor Vasarely, a Hungarian artist. But Bridget Riley is perhaps the best known of the op artists. Taking Vasarely's lead, she painted a number of works consisting only of black and white lines. Riley's paintings depict an unreal geometric world which frequently gives the impression of movement or color.

Apparent motion illusions are based on alternating optical contrasts (clear/dark, vertical/horizontal, left/right) to create a perturbation, like a visual overload perturbing the retinal circuits, which can, among other things, make our eyesight flicker.

Until now, we can count roughly four different families of relative movement or kinetic effects: phantom movements like moving flows, scintillating and popping-up patterns; floating images (such as the Ouchi illusion); rotating shapes (the B. Pinna and G. Brelstaff illusion); and self-moving and spontaneous rotating shapes (peripheral drift illusion). Let's go deeper into two of them.

Pinna rotating illusion

The Pinna-Brelstaff rotating illusion consists of two (or more) concentric rings of slanted lines or geometric shapes. When an observer moves towards the display the two rings of geometric patterns appear to counter-rotate. The illusion is optimal when there is a 66 degree orientation difference between elements composing the inner and outer rings. Three factors may cause this illusion: the luminance profile and the angular direction of the shapes and the bad integration of motion signals in our brain.

The peripheral drift illusion

This illusion was first described by the scientists A. Fraser and K. Wilcox, and by J. Faubert. The most famous peripheral drift illusion designed by A. Kitaoka is called Rotating Snakes. It consists of concentric repeating patterns of white, yellow, black and blue which evoke a striking illusion of motion. What makes this illusion so interesting is the fact that you are experiencing movement in the periphery, although you realize that the moving objects are not moving at all! While peripheral vision demonstrates movement over the entire field of the display, focusing on one particular part of the illusion shows that it is stationary. There are no definite answers to explain this phenomenon, but the main characteristics of the illusion are:

1 Illusory motion appears from a black region to the adjacent dark-gray region or from a white region to the adjacent light-gray region. Colors indicating the directions of illusory motion: black to dark gray or white to light gray.

2 It occurs well in peripheral vision. The object we fixate appears to be stationary.

3 It occurs well with stimuli of edges. Stimuli of smooth luminance profiles give weak illusions.

4 It occurs well with fragmented or curved edges. Stimuli made up of long edges give weak illusions.

5 It may be generated by involuntary halting eye movements.

Some apparent movement illusions contained in this book work better on a computer screen (because of the luminance), so you can try scanning them and watch them on your PC. You can also use these illusions as a resource or inspiration to design new illusory moving patterns. If you find a new pattern or a new way to enhance illusory motion, it would be great to hear from you!

'Mr. Speaker, I withdraw my statement that half the cabinet are asses. Half the cabinet are not asses'

– Benjamin Disraeli.

RIGHT OR WRONG? (the paradox of images)

Optical illusions can be useful to interest people in exploring and following logic and mathematical topics. On the following pages, we will present some "impossible" or paradoxical perception puzzles and self-working visual trick puzzles based on misconceptions and misperception. This means you'll be able to experience the persuasive powers of the images and learn how a picture can sidetrack your senses of reasoning! We will also take the opportunity to deal with self-referential images and graphic words.

What exactly are vanish puzzles? Vanish puzzles (we've renamed them "stereophanic puzzles") have existed for five centuries, but they still continue to amaze everyone! They can be of two types: figurative vanish puzzles and geometric vanish puzzles. Figurative

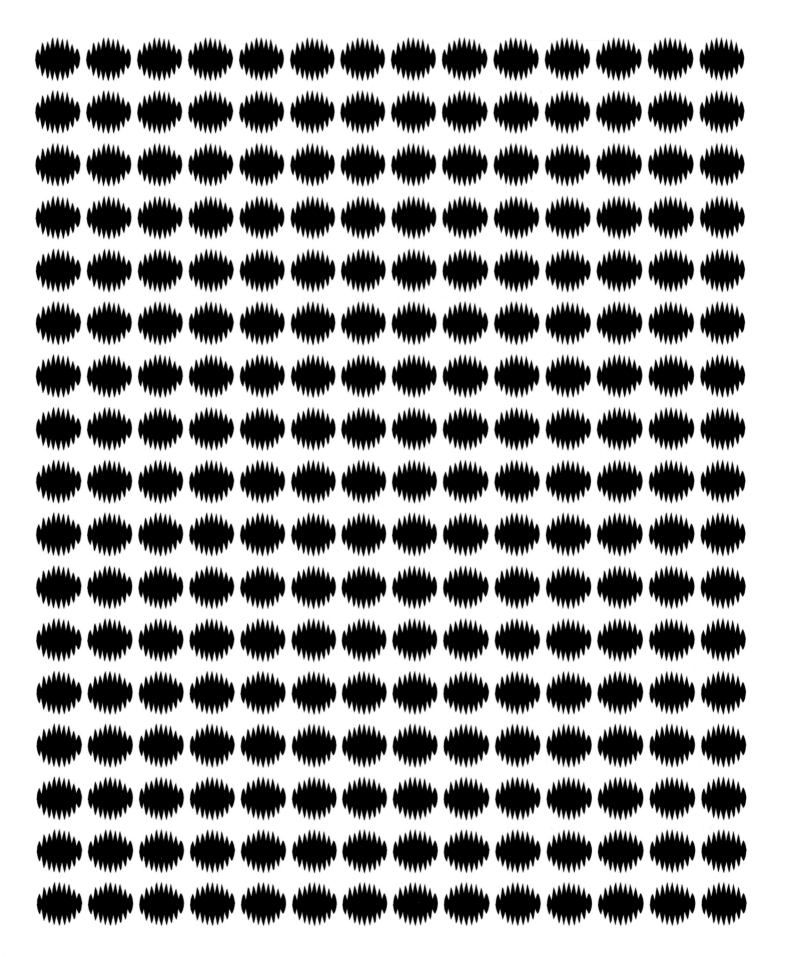

vanish puzzles involve the rearranging of parts of a puzzle representing a scene with a series of elements (people, animals, etc.) so that once the rearrangement is complete, an element of the scene disappears (or reappears). Geometric vanish puzzles involve either the apparent disappearance of a part of their surface or an apparent reducing of their area when the pieces of the puzzles are rearranged.

The first example of vanishing area puzzles was discovered in the book *Libro d'Architettura Primo* by Sebastiano Serlio, an Italian architect of the Renaissance, even though Serlio didn't notice that any area had actually vanished! The first description and explanation of this paradox was found in a maths puzzle book with a long title: *Rational Recreations in which the Principles of Numbers and Natural Philosophy are Clearly and Copiously Elucidated, by a Series of Easy, Entertaining, Interesting Experiments among which are all those Commonly Performed with the Cards* (1774) by William Hooper.

Because of their visual impact, vanish puzzles are really striking, but their mechanism is quite simple: the part (figure, surface) which disappears is simply redistributed differently on the remaining parts of the puzzle, confirming Lavoisier's law which says, 'In nature, nothing is created, nothing is lost, all is transformed.' Then, the magic is only based on the visual persuasion that the puzzle is really different after manipulation. Well, vanish puzzles are just one aspect of perception puzzles. In this book, you will find some new games and magic tricks directly involving visual perception or visual memory.

A self-reference occurs when an object refers to itself. Reference is possible when there are two logical levels of interpretation which can sometimes interfere with each other (contradiction). So self-referential statements can lead to paradoxes. Many self-referential paradoxes are hidden in our everyday life. They are like optical illusions; they seem normal, but when you examine them closely, the incongruity becomes obvious!

On the following pages, we have prepared a small selection of intriguing visual self-reference puzzles for you that are guaranteed to raise a smile if you give them enough thought. Do we have any doubt about that? Well, yes and no…

So dive in and enjoy some fantastic optical illusions. And if you get stuck, there are answers and explanations at the end of each gallery.

Blackout (left)

You may see hues of colors on the background of this pattern. Interestingly, if you scan this pattern in high-resolution color, your scanner will also reproduce colors! This effect occurs because the alternating small black and white spokes give intermittent stimulation to color receptors in our retina. Sometimes these stimuli interfere with each other producing a subjective color illusion.

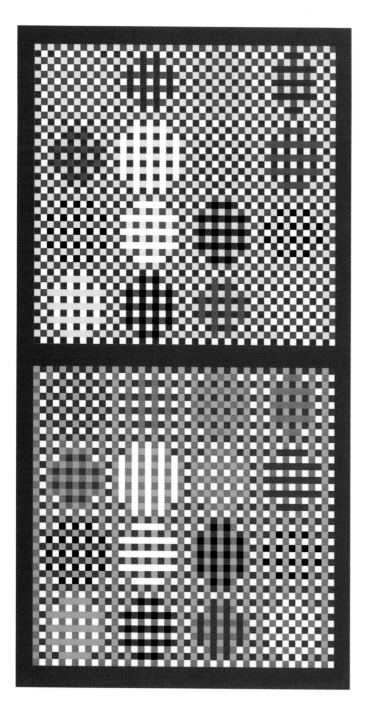

Pixelling

With only three colors, plus black and white, we can create a huge variety of apparent colors due to color contrast and color assimilation effects. The first table is composed of primary colors (red, blue and yellow); the second one, of secondary colors (green, violet, orange). View the tables from a certain distance to see the effects. Primary colors can create apparent secondary colors such as orange and green; whereas secondary colors can create primary colors such as blue or yellow.

Restaurant oddities

Find six critical errors in the picture! (Answer on page 44).

Dali for ever
Place the image in front of a mirror. What do you observe? (Answer on page 44).

Unspiral

Which one of these figures is a spiral?

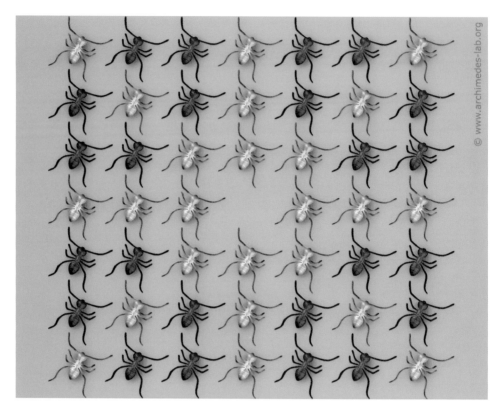

Ant square

At a glance, would you say there are more red ants or white ants?

Talking cups

These cups are telling the story of an unexpected encounter. Can you summarize it?

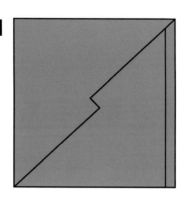

Paradoxical hole

Explain why, when three pieces of the square shown in fig. 1 are arranged as illustrated in fig. 3, we obtain the same square but with a mysterious hole!

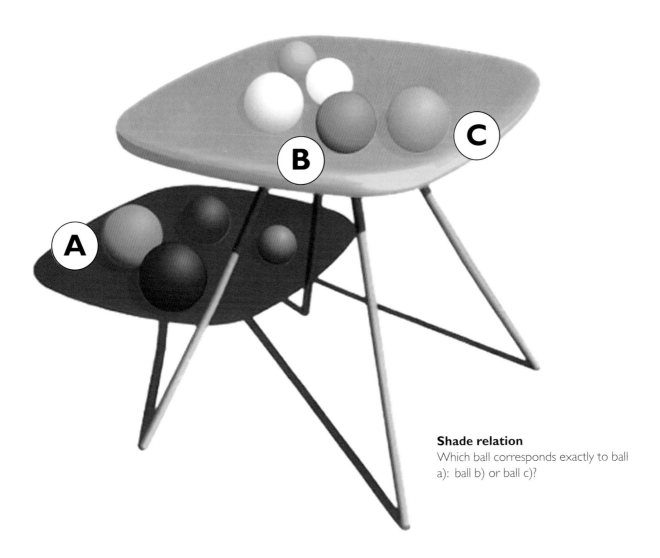

Shade relation
Which ball corresponds exactly to ball
a): ball b) or ball c)?

Magic Glass?
Find a way to remove one of the glasses from the tray completely.

Just oddities
Spot four oddities in the picture!

Every way takes you up!
You can go up in two opposite directions on these magic stairs...

Bilateral pool

The diver makes a jump into the fourth dimension and enters the water from the underside (turn the page upside-down).

Imaginary pin-up
I bet some of you wish this pin-up girl was really there. Sorry, it's just your imagination...

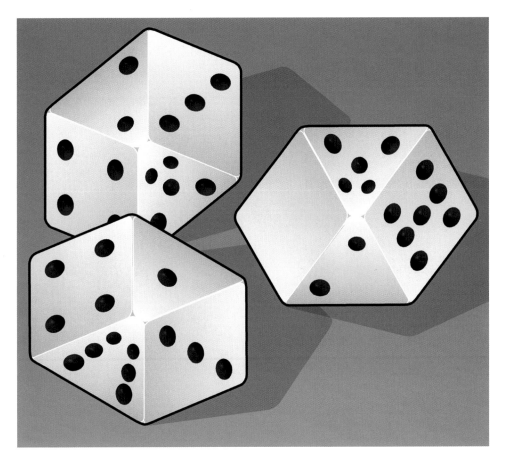

Impossible cubic dice
These are unreal four-dimensional, eight-sided dice (the eight sides are numbered by dots from 0 to 7, so placed that the sum of the dots on opposite sides equals 7).

Impossible steel tribar and rings

Tribar and rings

A 'classic' impossible tribar with two strange rings slipped on to one of its bars. As you can see, the rings are perspectively incoherent.

Z-odd pentagon

The Z-shaped board intersects the pentagon at three impossible points.

©99, G. Sarcone, www.archimedes-lab.

Distorted?
Is anything in the picture straight?

Apparent rotations

Move your eyes around the clock and the gears will appear to rotate. Circular objects, including radial repeating patterns with "sawtooth" luminance profiles, produce a sensation of motion called peripheral drift illusion. A. Kitaoka, a Japanese perception scientist, specializes in designing such illusory patterns (you can see his work at: http://www.psy.ritsumei.ac.jp/~akitaoka/). However, this kind of illusion works even better when it is sufficiently enlarged or seen on a computer screen.

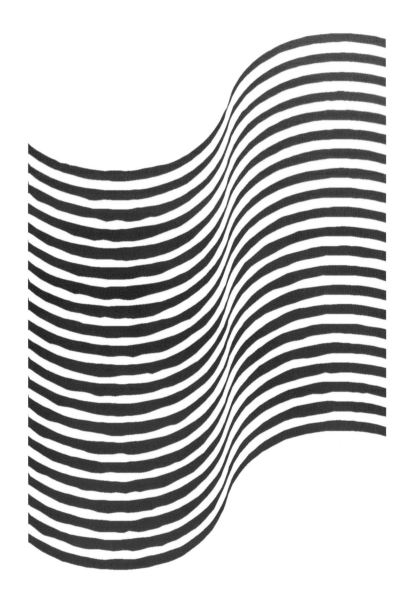

A tribute to da Vinci
Leonardo's face is hidden in the stripes – can you see it?

Impossible vault

Push or pull? Your money wouldn't be safe in this vault!

Gallery 1 Notes

Page 25

1 The Coca-Cola (Coca-Coca) logo on the bottle.
2 The top of the glass stands in front of the bottle while the stem is behind.
3 The writing on the ashtray contains "is" twice: Smoking is is hazardous to your health.
4 The ashtray has an impossible geometric shape.
5 The handle of the coffee cup.
6 The teeth of the fork (are there three or four teeth? Maybe both!).

Page 26

This image looks the same when seen in the mirror! This kind of word is called a reflection ambigram. A surprising number of words offer this type of symmetry when written, such as: TOOT, MOM...

Page 27

Neither of them, because they're both perfect concentric circles!

Page 28

You've probably answered that there are more white ants as they are more scattered throughout the picture... the colored ants are, however, equal in number! Another illusion is that the square made up of ants seems to tilt slightly to the left.

Page 29

In the profile of the first cup (in the background) you can see the faces of two frowning people who meet each other unexpectedly. In the second cup, we can see that they are sticking out their tongues at each other; and finally, in the third cup, they laugh and go off to have a drink together. Maybe they were old friends!

Page 30

If you could stack square A on the top of 'square' B, you'd see a tiny difference (in red). This difference represents the area of the hole in 'square' B. So nothing disappeared, the missing piece is just redistributed in the whole area of 'square' B (square B isn't actually a square, but a rectangle).

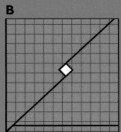

Page 31

Ball c), even if it seems a darker than ball a). This is a simultaneous lightness contrast effect.

Page 32

Just turn the image upside-down and the wine glass will be seen standing outside the tray. Amazing, isn't it? This image was invented by Gianni Sarcone for a science festival on optical illusions.

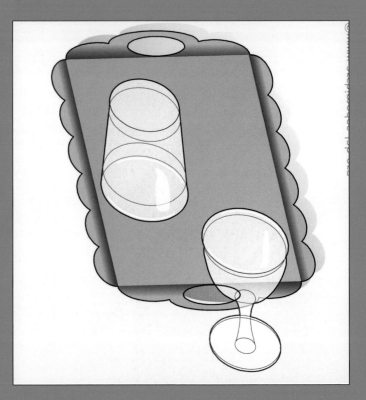

Page 33

1 The upper part of the hourglass is outside the rung, the lower part is behind it.
2 The top of the transparent vase stands in front of the pitcher while the bottom is behind the books.
3 The bottom of the vase on the right doesn't correspond perspectively to its opening.
4 The books appear to be two or three at the same time.

Page 40

The checkered frames are perfectly straight. The small white and black squares create layouts of 'subliminal' oblique lines which interfere with the orthogonal outlines of the frames creating the bulging illusion. If you observe the picture with half-closed eyes, you can perceive these 'subliminal' oblique lines similar to the blurred figure below. This is a neat version of the Zölner illusion.

Page 42
To see the three-dimensional face of da Vinci view the image from a distance of six feet (two metres). Each stripe contains a small portion of information about Leonardo's face. Our brain gathers and interprets all this partial information and then assembles it as one unique image.

Page 43
This is an impossible figure illusion: the lower side of the reinforced door is opening away from you, while the upper side is opening towards you.

Gallery II

Ambiguous arrows
Figure-ground ambiguity.

Off-color cow
The color in this photograph of a cow is not balanced at all
(the left side is bluish and the right side has too much yellow).
To restore the balance, stare at the fly in the second diagram for
thirty seconds, then look at the cow again.

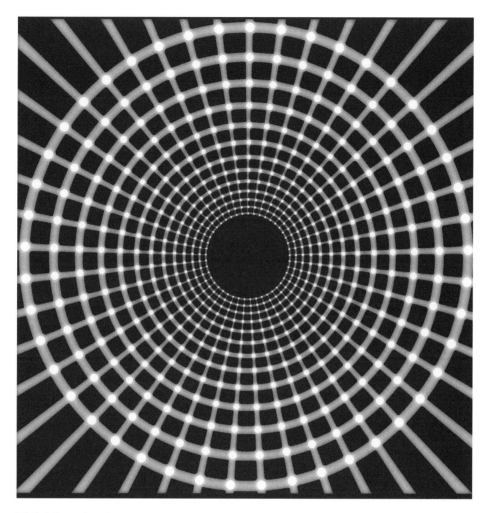

Twinkling circular pattern
In the above illustration, dark brown dots appear to form and vanish at the intersections of the gray circles and spokes when you scan your eyes across the image.

Real piano bar
An impossible scene for night revelers.

How many angels?

How many angels are in the picture?

Is this a Polar Bear or a Seal?

Both, actually! A polar bear crawling out of a hole in the ice and a
seal lying on the ice facing to the left...

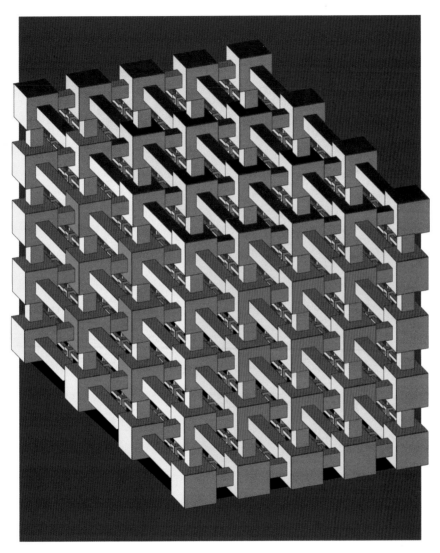

Peculiar cubic network
Actually, the network does not really represent the faces of a cube.

Animal magic
Can you find a second zebra?

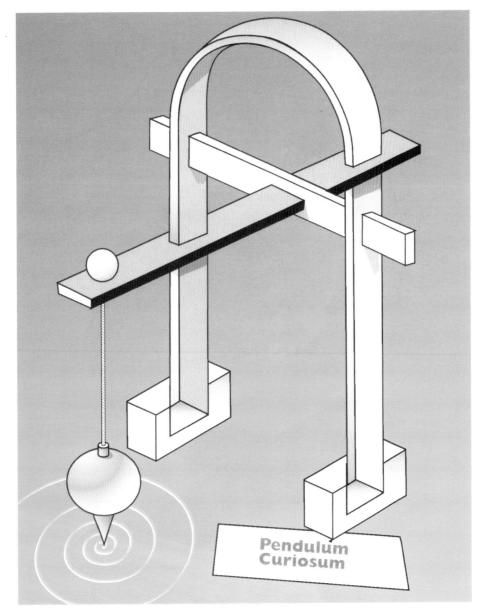

Impossible device

Just the incredible invention of a mad scientist...The feet of the object cannot exist in our 3D world, likewise the crossings of the boards.

Additional birds

Can you find ten birds within the picture?

The waiting
Is the rower being watched?

Impossible hidden discs

Can you find the two discs in the picture?

Anthropomorphic differences

Find two big differences between the boys. If you can't, turn the picture upside-down. Eeek!

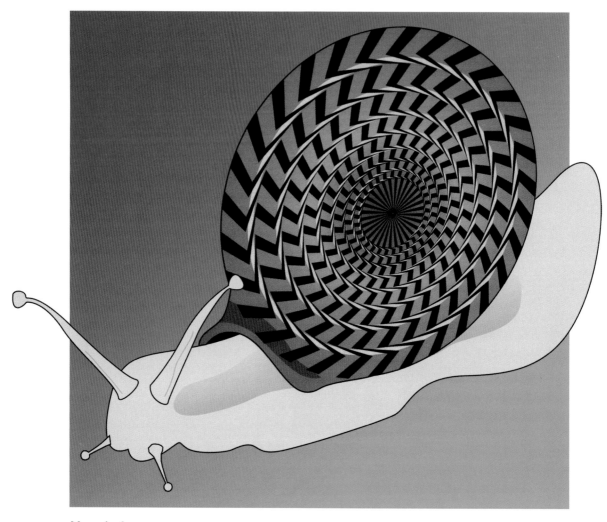

No spirals

The pattern on the snail shell is made up of concentric circles.

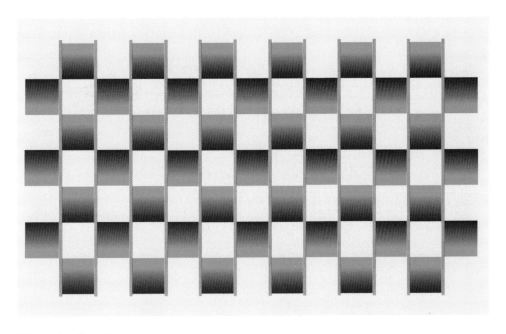

Diverging lines?

Are the vertical red lines straight and parallel to each other?

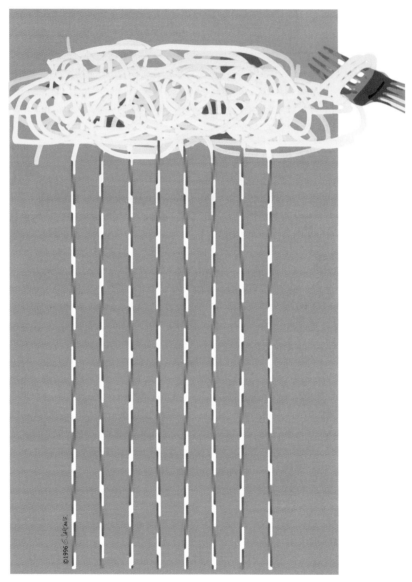

Spaghetti illusion
Do the vertical spaghetti bulge inwards or outwards?
Anyway, buon appetito!

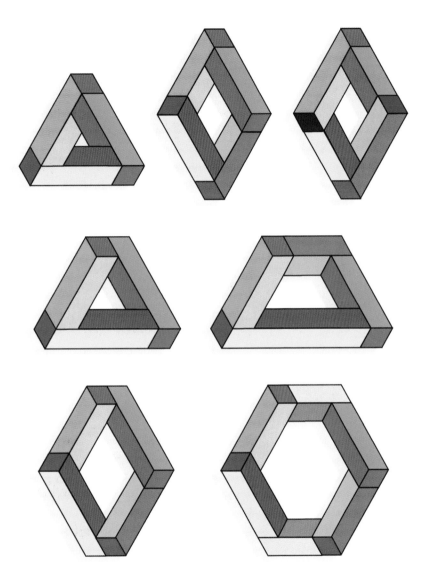

Impossible rod figures

If you want to keep children busy for a very long time, ask them to make these figures with Cuisenaire rods.

Phantom circles
The illusion of concentric ellipses is created by the connections
between the black strokes.

Female ubiquity
Are you looking at this woman from behind or face on?

Alien vision
If you glance at the woman out of the corner of your eye, you probably won't notice her double imaging.

Panoramic cube
The inside of the cube is outside, and vice versa.

PERCEPTION

Page 63

In the photograph on the cover, which we appear to see in this drawing, the figure seems to emerge against the brick of the wall...

Page 64
Two different pairs of angels

Page 65

When the face of the second figure is seen right side up, it appears quite innocuous because looking for familiar features seems natural. Strangely, his face still appears to us wrong when it is upside-down; the mouth and eyes, that don't change, depending on the angle they are viewed from. Our brains used to seeing faces right side up are unable to detect small changes in a face, but only pay attention to the position of the eyes, the mouth, and the nose. When the face is upside-down, our brains encounter a possibility of recognising and seeing the features differently.

Page 66

They are perfectly aligned and parallel, even though they appear to diverge...

They don't bulge at all. The effect can be seen in the central band of the illusion. The standard horizontal top was in fact described by J.J. Lingelbach as the checkerboard illusion...

This [singular] collection of illusions... pseudoptics. The twisted-cord
[shade] is probably due to orientation-sensitive simple cells in the
striate cerebral cortex, which interact to combine a set of small
closely-spaced tilted lines into one single tilted line.

Page 65

you can see her from behind, or if you hide the shaded arm with a
pencil (or any other oblong object) you will see her face-on.

Gallery III

Color frames

The frames with the + sign are the same color, even though they look different. This to illustrate that the same color affects us differently, depending on the adjacent colors. This visual effect is called simultaneous color contrast.

Zoltan's hankerchief

Zoltan is a conjuror and his favorite trick is to magically mend a
torn kerchief (as shown in the picture) by respecting perfectly its
pattern: when he performs the trick all the printed discs of the mended
kerchief coincide with each other. Try to imitate Zoltan: reproduce the
torn kerchief, and cut it into five pieces, so that when the pieces are
assembled they form a perfect square with 41 entire printed discs.

Souvenirs of Utopialand
There are five oddities in the picture...

Temple of confusion
All the tiles of the temple are obviously parallel and the circles in
the rosette perfectly concentric.

Crazy gymnasts

Can you spot three problems with what's going on here?

©www.archimedes-lab.org

Going up?
Could you get to the top of these stairs?

The puzzler
Can the tridimensional two-piece puzzle shown on the poster be completed? (Notice the special self-referential mirror...)

Pretzel of Time

Can you spot three real impossible objects in this scene?

Find the mouse...
The cat is looking for the mouse. Where is it?

Bizarre dogs
How many dogs can you count?

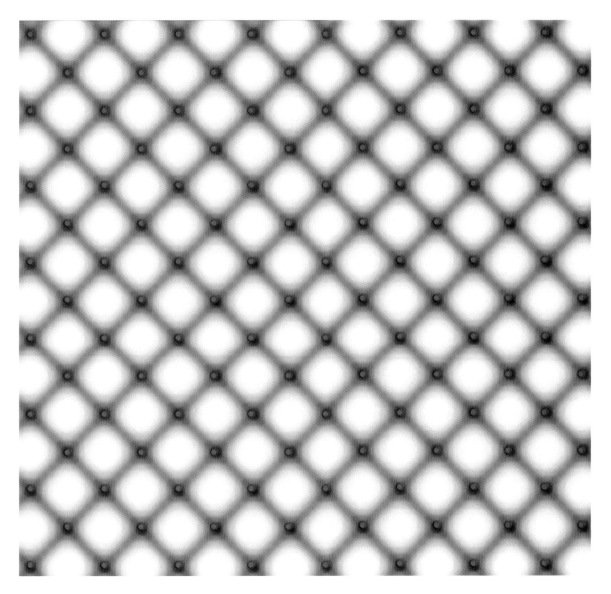

Vibrating red dots
Wow; can your eyes bear these apparent red flashes?

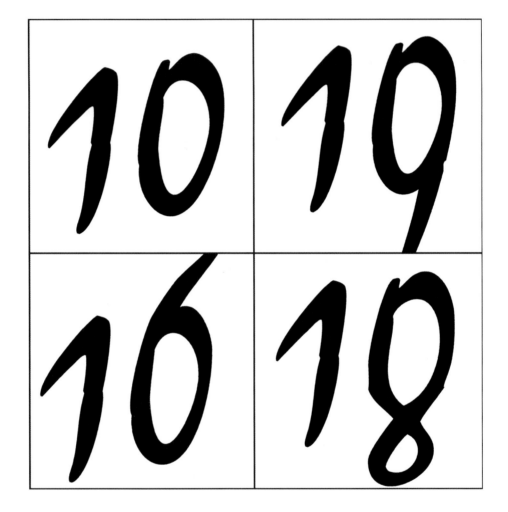

Magic 10

This trick relies on visual perception. Reproduce the picture on a cardboard sheet and cut out the four cards, each one containing a different number (10, 16, 18, and 19). Show the cards to a friend, then assemble and turn the cards over. Tell your friend that you have the mysterious ability to attract the number 10, and ask him to shuffle the deck and give you a card face down. Now show your card. Lo and behold, it represents the number 10! Can you guess how the trick works?

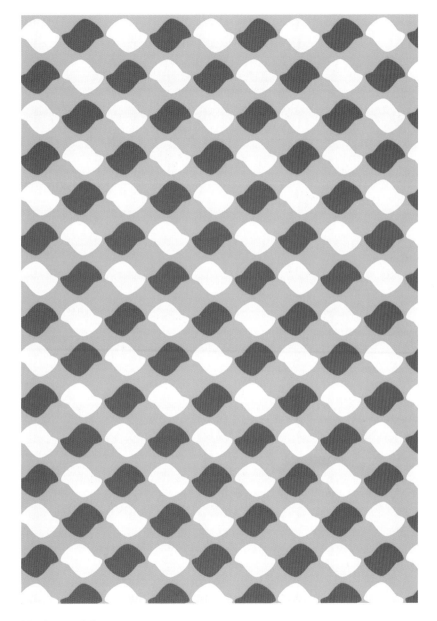

Horizontal flows

You may see flashing horizontal flows in this pattern.

Roman floor-mosaic

This is a copy of the oldest apparent moving pattern. The radiating pattern of tiered plumes seems to rotate slightly.

Bulging lines
The red lines appear to bulge slightly.

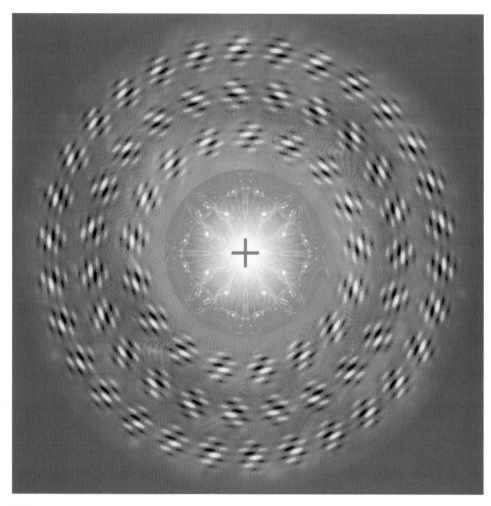

Pinna rotating effect

Some regular concentric objects appear to rotate when we approach or move back from them. Move your head backwards and forwards keeping the focus on the central cross of the image; the three circular patterns will counter-rotate!

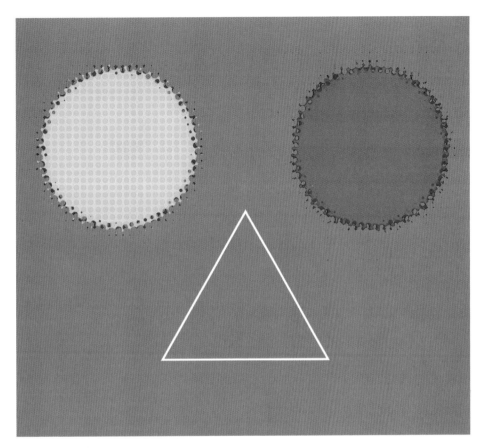

Retinal rivalry

Touch the triangle with the tip of your nose while staring at both colored discs. Now, you may see a unique disc... but can you say what color the disc is?

Bamboo effect
Are the yellow jointed stems of the bamboo canes really slightly concave?

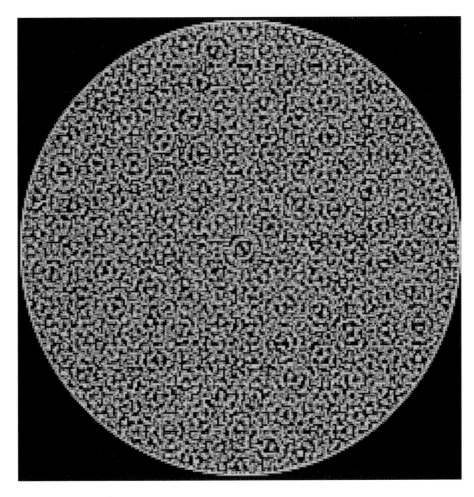

Undisciplined dots

Small circles seem to appear and disappear spontaneously as the eye is moved over the disc.

Concave or convex colander?

Depending on our point of view, the same object may appear concave or convex, as shown in the illustration.

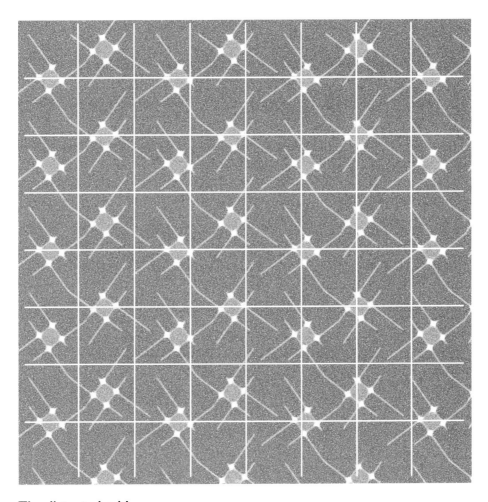

The distorted grid
Does the grid appear slightly distorted?

Gallery III Notes

Page 72

Page 73

1 The columns seem to be either cylindrical or parallelepipedic;
2 The cart of the boy has an impossible shape;
3 The upper part of the bird fountain appears in front of the column, the lower part behind;
4 The stairs appear to descend in a continuous loop;
5 The water jet passes through the banister.

Page 75

1 The two gymnasts performing on the parallel bars have two incompatible perspectives
2 At each side of the platform can you count one or two steps? Are they perspectively ascending or descending?
3 The man who performs with the cord: does he really lean on the board to keep his balance?

Page 76

This drawing of an impossible staircase was inspired by Escher's work. Although the staircase is conceptually impossible, it does not interfere with our perception of it. Actually, the paradox is not even apparent to many people!

Page 77

No; it is an impossible figure.

Page 78

Have a closer look at:
1 The teeth of the gear wheels;
2 The belt, especially in the upper part of the drawing where it forms a kind of pretzel;
3 The axis of the wheel.

Page 79

The mouse is IN the cat. Actually, cat and mouse share the same mouth and moustaches... The eyes of the mouse are represented by the two clear spots; the ears, by the cat's eyes.

Page 80

Don't count them. This is just a canine impossible figure!

Page 81

This scintillating effect is related to the Lingelbach grid illusion.

Page 82

The probability is one to four that the card you receive features the number 10. If you don't happen to have a 10, but a 18 (or a 19), just hide the lower loop of the 8 (or the downstroke of the 9) with your thumb and present the card as illustrated in A. If the number on the card is 16, hide the upstroke of the number 6 with your forefinger and present the card to your friend as shown in B.

Page 83

The illusion of flows occurs when we look at certain patterns containing contrasting colors. The effect is due to the lateral inhibition of our visual system.

Page 84

The first attempt to create apparent movement with static images was done by Roman mosaic craftsmen. This copy of a Roman floor-mosaic had in its center the head of the Medusa.

Page 85

The square patterns give the impression of bending forward along with the red lines.

Page 86

This illusion is also called the Pinna-Brelstaff rotating illusion. Bad integration of motion signals in our brain may be one of the causes of this rotation illusion.

Page 87

The two colors will not be mixed as one might think. So, the disc is 'magreenta', Alternately green and magenta because of the retinal rivalry. And if you move back slowly while staring at the test image, you may see a 'magreenta' disc floating between the two other discs.

Page 88

No; the bamboo canes are perfectly straight. Yellow color has a low spatial resolution; that means it is difficult for our brains to correctly define a determined yellow shape on a clear background. We aren't capable of seeing the vertical yellow stems as straight lines, because they tend to pull in and appear slightly curved inwards. The black inclusions enhance this concave effect.

Page 89

This visual popping-up activity is due to our visual system which is constantly searching for the best interpretation in this unorganized pattern.

Page 90

Shadows influence depth perception. We tend to assume light is coming from above; that's why when the shadow of the colander is at the top, we believe it is concave, and when the shadow is inverted, we believe it is convex.

Page 91

The grid is perfectly straight. The Japanese pattern in the background is responsible for this distortion illusion. This is a smart variant of the Zöllner lines illusion.

Gallery IV

Totems

Are the stacked rectangular threatening figures of both totems perfectly aligned and parallel to each other? The stacked rectangular figures seem to tilt slightly, but they are parallel and aligned to each other. This illusion is related to the café wall illusion.

Rome to Paris

Ah, Paris, Paris... Are the signposts diverging at the top (where the signs are fixed)?

The incredible secret of perpetual motion
Turn the page over and you will discover the secret of perpetual motion.

The incredible secret of perpetual motion

Flip the page back and you will discover the secret of perpetual motion.

Triangular dovetail
The assembly shown in the picture looks like an impossible construction. However, try to imagine how the pieces were assembled.

Invisible triangles
Can you perceive six triangles in this Kanisza-like figure?

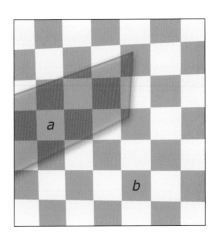

Simultaneous Brightness Contrasts
A patchwork of examples of simultaneous brightness contrasts. Every picture illustrates a particular case wherein a brightness contrast occurs. In each case, square a) and square b) are exactly the same shade.

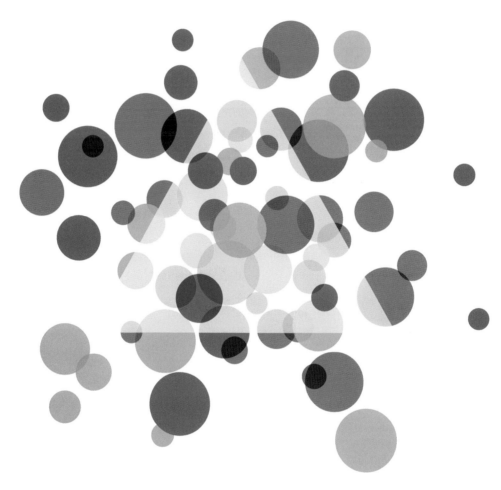

Ghost Triangle
The white background looks brighter within the triangle area, but that's just an illusion. The ghostly translucent triangle actually doesn't exist at all, its outline is only determined by some colored balls!

Cubic Colors

The texture of an object can influence the color shades. The picture illustrates that the same red color can be perceived differently depending on the texture of the cube (consider only the top side of the cubes).

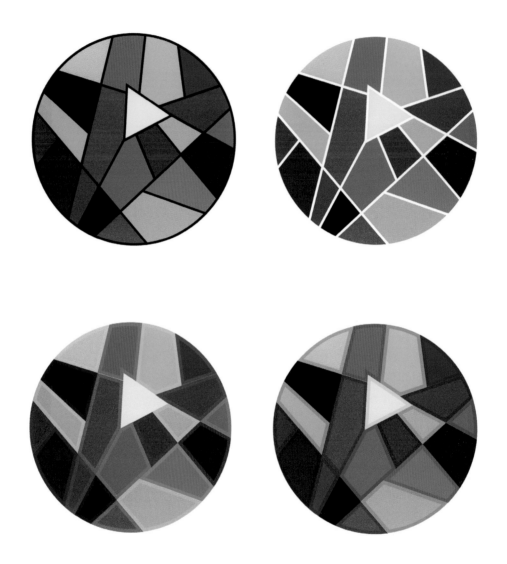

Framed colors
Frames and borderlines can subjectively modify the shade of a color patchwork. In all four examples the colors are exactly the same; only the color (black, white) and the shade (bright, dark) of the borderlines change!

Hue induction

The yellow triangular tile is exactly the same in all four examples,
but seems to change slightly when the hues of the bordering colors are
altered. In general, a color looks most colorful against other colors in lower lightness.

Brightness contrast in an everyday scene

The tiles a), b) and c) are all the same shade, despite the fact they look very different! Brightness contrast is an effect in which a color of given brightness will look darker on a light background and brighter on a dark background.

Shrinking circles
When you scan the picture with your eyes, the circles in the disc seem to shrink.

Peripheral drift illusion
Concentric repeating color patterns can induce a sensation of rotation. In figure A, however, the rotational movement is cancelled because of the conflicting luminance gradients of the concentric patterns. In B, to make the disc rotate you have to follow with your eyes the arrows placed beside the disc.

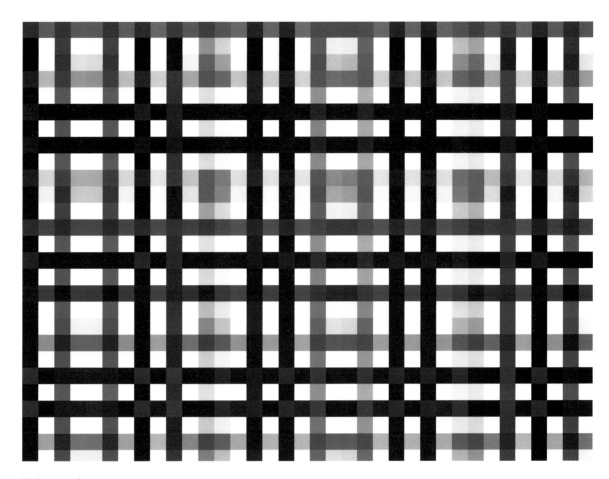

Shimmering texture

This texture seems to shimmer, especially within the intersections of the dark blue bands.

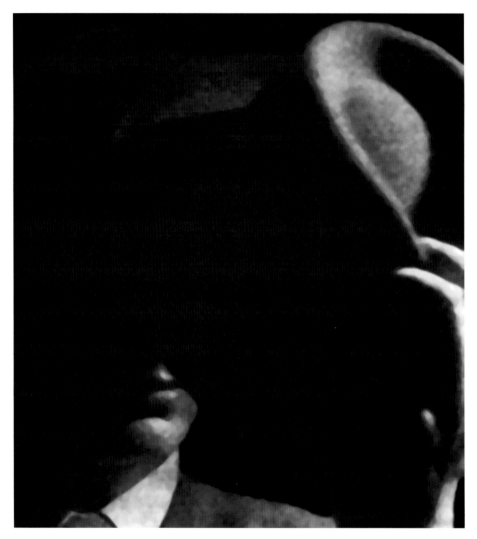

Perceptual set

"Perceptual set" is a predisposition to perceive something in relation to prior perceptual experiences. Thanks to our prior perception experiences we can see in the picture...

Uniform red?
Are all the tessellated red squares the same shade?

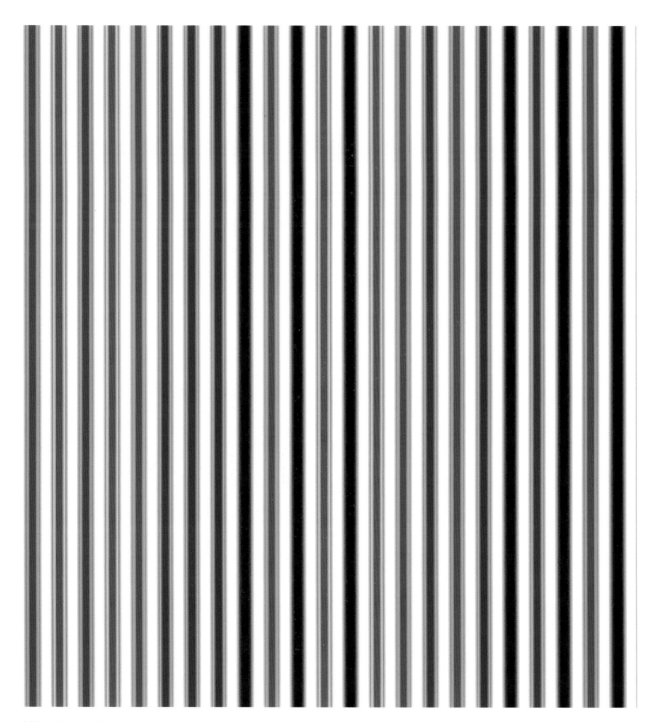

Vibrating colors

These color pipes seem to vibrate and move spontaneously. Now move your
head backwards and forwards, keeping the focus on the center of the
image; the pipes will dramatically expand and become bold! (The effect is even more
apparent on a PC screen).

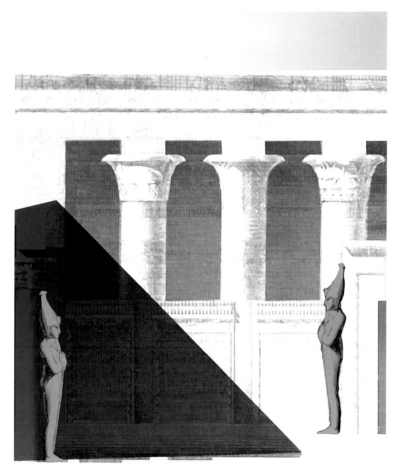

Egyptian shades
Which statue of the Pharaoh seems darker?

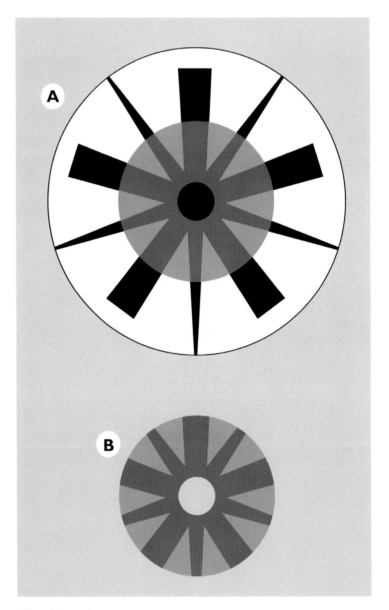

Blending colors

Both gray discs in A and B are similar. However, the shades in the gray disc in A appear to blend together and to be less contrasted than disc B. The shades in disc B seem flat.

You rang?
Which button seems darker?

Gallery IV Notes

Page 96
No, they are perfectly parallel!. Take a ruler and verify them. This is another version of the twisted cords illusion.

Page 99

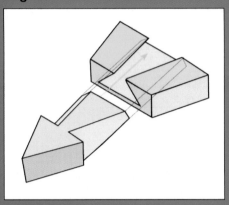

Pages 97-98
Pages 97 and 98 are examples of a perfect self-referential joke. Self-referential sentences are a kind of verbal illusion.

Page 102
This closure illusion is a variation of the well-known Kanisza triangle. The entire translucent triangle that covers some colored balls is created by our visual system. The effect is also called subjective or illusory contours.

Page 107
This kind of apparently self-moving shape is related to peripheral drift illusion.

Page 109
This effect is similar to the Herman grid illusion and is due to lateral inhibition.

Page 110
A man with a hat, even though the picture is mostly dark and incomplete.

Page 111
Yes, they are the same shade.
Although each individual red square possesses the identical shade (left and right), when combined in a tessellated pattern (middle), the second alignment of squares is always perceived as darker than the first alignment of squares. This illusion is related to the Anstis and Watanabe diamond illusion.

Page 112
The vibrating flows are mainly due to lateral inhibition.

Page 113
They are both the same shade.

Page 115
They are exactly the same color. It is an incredible simultaneous brightness contrast effect.

Gallery V

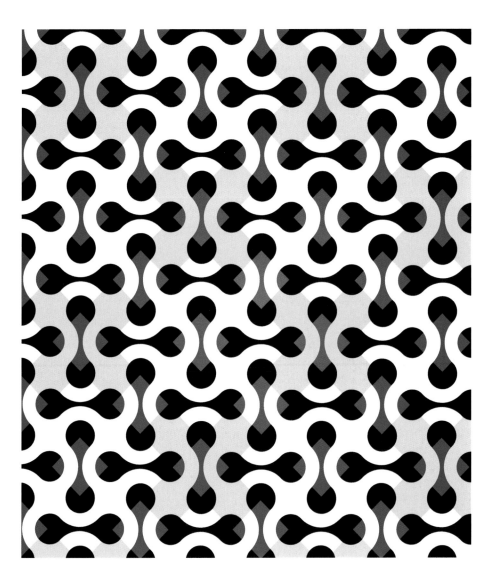

Hypnotic neon lights

Do you see a pattern of large and small squares? The apparent neon squares seem to pulse slightly when we concentrate on the image. I say apparent neon squares because the wavy pattern gives you the impression that there are whole squares lying behind it. But as the entire design lies on the same plane, the apparently pulsating squares are really just segmented colored shapes. Neon color spreading contains illusory contours, brightness induction, color assimilation and perceptual transparency which gives depth perception. D. Varin first observed such an illusion (in 1971), but the name "neon color" came from H. Van Tuijl. The human ability to perceive a neon effect may be a remnant of the development of our power of sight under water at extreme depths, as there is a lack of light there.

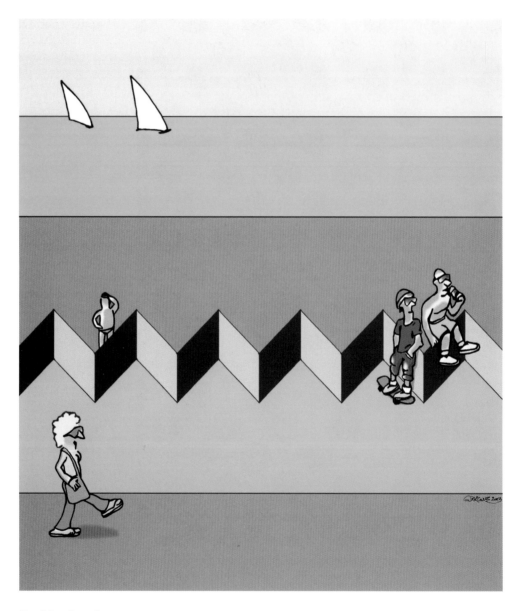

Bathing huts?
The walking woman and the skateboard kid obviously aren't on the same plane...

How many triangles?
How many triangles can you perceive in the picture?

A

B

Herman grids

In grid A, we see little bright smudges appear at the intersections of the black bars which vanish when we look at them. Strangely, when we tilt the grid as shown in B, the effect weakens, but we can now perceive bright diagonals crossing each white diamond-shaped box which give the impression of a series of vertical lines (see the blue highlighted example).

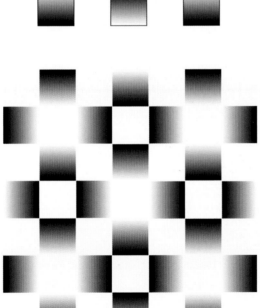

Sheen and halo effects
Using the same square composition with and without outlines, we can obtain two very different visual effects.

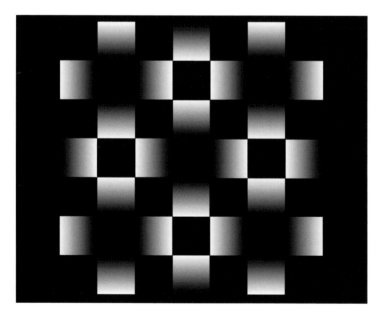

Halo and black hole effects
Using the same square composition in positive and negative, we can obtain two opposite visual effects.

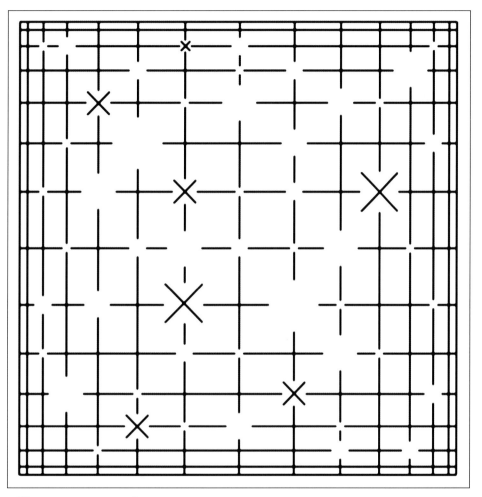

Illusory squares and spots
Can you see squares and bright spots?

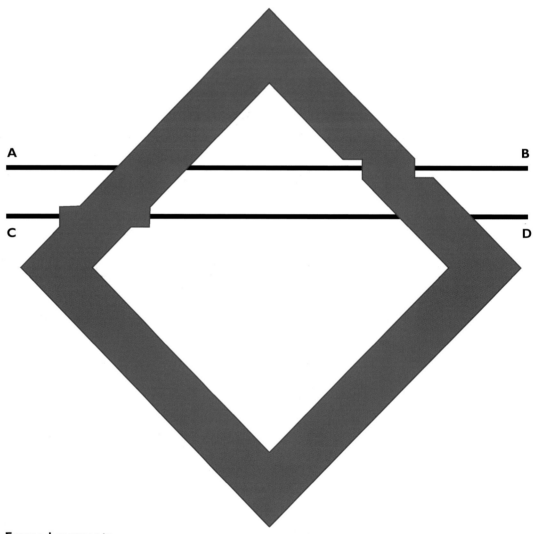

Framed segments
The two segments AB and CD go through the frame. Is segment AB perfectly straight? What about segment CD?

Light Grid

This is a variant of the "Hypnotic neon lights"; we have inverted the colors (black-blue) and this time we are able to see an apparent "neon spreading" grid. But you will note the pulsating effect is absent.

A

B

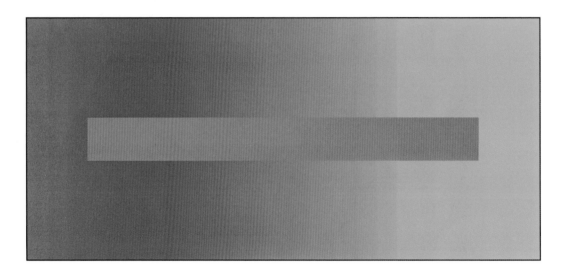

Color Contrast

Which bar (A or B) corresponds to the bar
lying on the contrasted
background?

A

B

99	98	97	96	95	94	93	92	91	90
89	88	87	86	85	84	83	82	81	80
79	78	77	76	75	74	73	72	71	70
69	68	67	66	65	64	63	62	61	60
59	58	57	56	55	54	53	52	51	50
49	48	47	46	45	44	43	42	41	40
39	38	37	36	35	34	33	32	31	30
29	28	27	26	25	24	23	22	21	20
19	18	17	16	15	14	13	12	11	10

Mind-reading powers

Marie-Jo and I will perform a magical and real mind reading trick. Follow our instructions and... relax!

Concentrate on the colored disc (A) with the strange signs inside it for 10 seconds. Cool... Now think of any number between 10 and 99 (example: 24). Add both digits together (2 + 4 = 6). Then subtract this total from your original choice (24 - 6 = 18). When you get the total, look up the number (18) on the chart above. Find the two corresponding symbols and focus on them.

Concentrate.

Concentrate... OK, turn to page 140 and you will be convinced that we are able to read your mind!

Did we get it right? Want another go? Turn the page...

A

B

99	98	97	96	95	94	93	92	91	90
89	88	87	86	85	84	83	82	81	80
79	78	77	76	75	74	73	72	71	70
69	68	67	66	65	64	63	62	61	60
59	58	57	56	55	54	53	52	51	50
49	48	47	46	45	44	43	42	41	40
39	38	37	36	35	34	33	32	31	30
29	28	27	26	25	24	23	22	21	20
19	18	17	16	15	14	13	12	11	10

Next page!

Again, here you have to concentrate on the colored disc containing the arcane signs (A)... and think of any number between 10 and 99 (example: 72). Sum both digits together (7 + 2 = 9). Then subtract this total from your original choice (72 - 9 = 63). When you get the total, look up the number (63) on the chart above. Find the two corresponding symbols and focus on them. Concentrate. Concentrate... and turn to page 140 for the answer.

Tints and backgrounds

You can see three distinctly tinted color samples in the picture, but when placed on the multicolored background, the distinction seems to diminish dramatically.

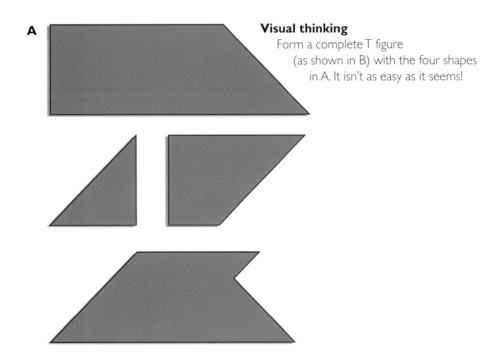

Visual thinking
Form a complete T figure
(as shown in B) with the four shapes
in A. It isn't as easy as it seems!

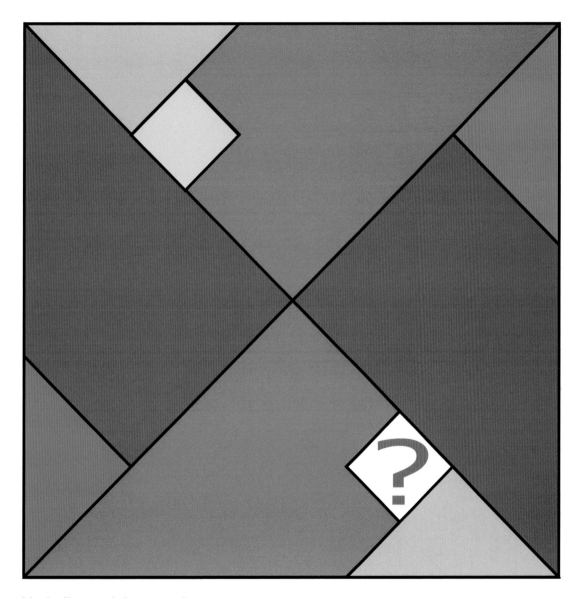

Magically mend the square!
The idea is to cut up the nine-piece color puzzle and reassemble its
pieces to form a square again without the hole in it!

Find the prism
The outlines of the prism are
hidden in the picture...

Impossible spiral
Is this a right-angled spiral?

Tribar

Try to build this tribar by following the visual instruction (take a close look at the screws and the washers...)

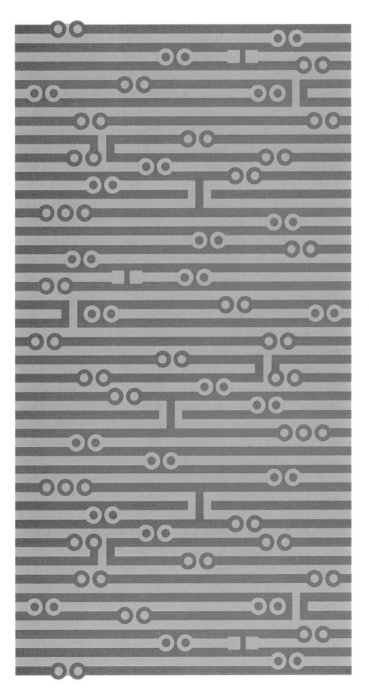

Ambiguous circuits

At a glance, you may say the background of the circuit board is blue, but are you sure?

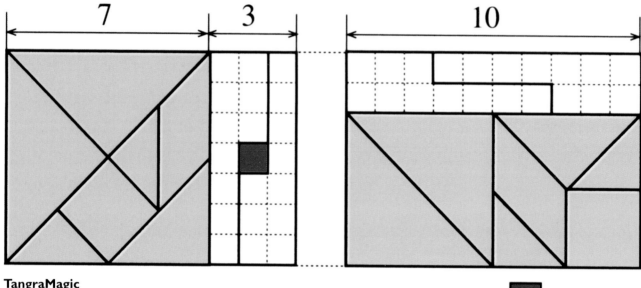

TangraMagic

This is a ten-piece puzzle. The Tangram is actually only the part in gray. With the addition of two long, L-shaped pieces and a small red square, the entire combined figure forms a rectangle. Note that the base of the rectangle is 10 units long. What is strange is that we can assemble the rectangle without the small red square and even in this case the area appears almost identical. How can you explain this?

The mischievous Leprechaun

Position yourself approximately 30 centimetres in front of the diagram. Close your right eye and with the other focus on each number one at a time. Count up at one-second intervals. By the time you get to number 4, the Leprechaun may seem to have wandered off the circle.

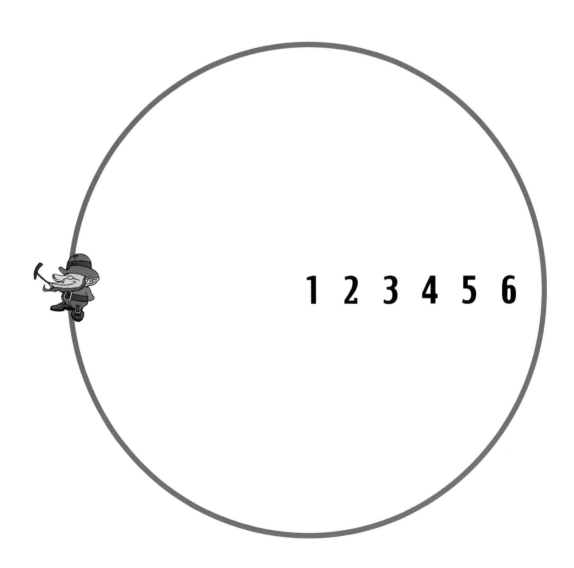

Gallery V Notes

Page 121

There are at all 11 triangles: three small white triangles, three small colored triangles, three large colored triangles, and two illusory bright triangles.

Page 122

Up until now, there are no definite answers to explain the apparition of bright smudges on the grid. One much-debated theory suggests that the contrast between the white boxes and the black spaces makes the spaces appear blacker. At the intersections there are no adjacent, contrasting white sections, so the black spaces appear a bit less black, hence the 'grayish' effect.

Page 125

On this grid you can see several Xs; the four points of each X determine an illusory square. You may also notice areas of apparent bright discs that actually don't exist. These illusions are related to the Kanisza triangle illusion. These illusory figures depend on "gaps" in the grid lines.

Page 126

Both segments are perfectly straight. Strangely, the portion of segment AB which enters from A (on the left) doesn't appear to be in alignment with the whole segment. The same applies to segment CD. The portion which enters from D (on the right) doesn't appear to be aligned with the rest.

Page 128

This illusion is based on the simultaneous color contrast effect. The green bar on the contrasted background is the same shade throughout. Therefore the answer is bar A.

Page 129

The image above shows the two symbols you thought of, right?

Page 130

We guessed right again, didn't we?

How it works

We mislead your attention using images. Yes, you concentrate on images, but the trick is based on a simple math rule. To understand this magic trick, try doing it again and again. (Hint: why are the numbers on the chart you use to select the symbols all multiples of 9?)

Page 131

This color experiment shows you that different tints are more difficult to distinguish on a colored background than on an uniform background.

Page 132

It's difficult to judge the correct position of the diagonal shape which joins the other pieces together because we tend to concentrate more readily on the horizontal and vertical aspect of the world around us than the diagonal.

Page 133

Page 134

approximately 4.95 × 9.9 = 49. The discrepancy is equal to 50 − 49 = 1 square unit which is the area of the red square.

A short history of the Tangram… Little is known for certain about the origin of the Tangram. Even the origin of the name is obscure! The earliest known book was published around 1813 in China. A Tangram-like puzzle first appeared in a book published in Japan in 1742. Scholars assume that Tangrams originated from the Orient before the 18th century and then spread westward. Frankly, in my humble opinion, a lot of "oriental" games were first created in Europe and then readapted in Asia, like the "Chinese checker" called *tiao-qi* in China. In the past, the adjective "Chinese" was commonly used to denote any odd, complicated or contrived thing and not the origin of the object! However, by 1817, Tangram publications had appeared in the United States and in Europe. Whatever date the Tangram was invented, you have to know that rearrangement puzzle roots can be traced back to the 3rd century BC! Back in those days Archimedes, a Greek mathematican, designed a Tangram-like puzzle called *Loculus Archimedis* or *Ostomachion*.

Page 139

In our visual field there is a very large spot, called the blind spot, where the optical nerve enters the eye. This region has no photoreceptors… So, when the Leprechaun enters your blind spot he naturally disappears (from view).

Page 137

The background is either blue or red. It's a kind of undecidable figure.

Page 138

In the second diagram, the Tangram appears to occupy 10 × 5 = 50 square units, while it is clear from the first diagram that the area of the Tangram occupies a square area of 7 × 7 = 49 square units. If the gray rectangular Tangram portion is packed tightly and measured, you will find that it is slightly less than the apparent 10 × 5 dimensions. Actually the real area of the gray rectangle is

Gallery VI

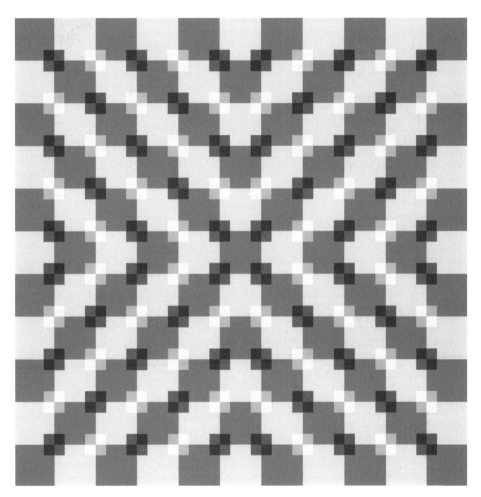

Bulging square
Is it a convex square?

The small dark and light squares on the foreground create a "subliminal" crossing pattern that constrains the alignment of squares on the background to appear slightly bulging. This illusion is related to the Zöllner illusion. You can perceive the "subliminal" crossing pattern by looking at the picture with half-closed eyes.

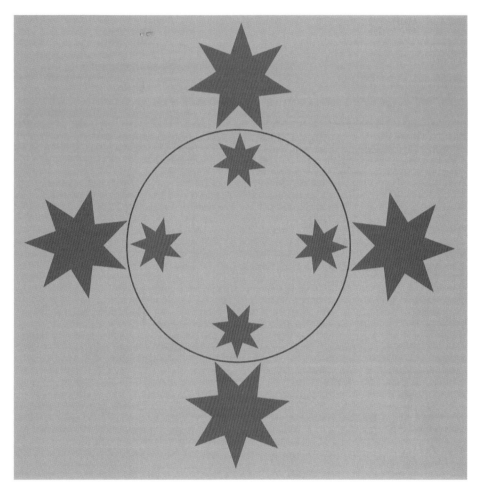

Perfect circle?
Is the red circle really 'circular'?

Fooling cross
Are the segments AB and CD the same length?

Floating flakes
Are the lines of floating flakes perfectly parallel? Do they move imperceptibly up and down?

Verbal illusions

Why is the sign paradoxical? And what about the message on the bottle?

Both objects contain a paradoxical self-referential sentence.

A sentence is said to be self-referential when it refers to itself. It illustrates somewhat the relationship between meaning and the symbolism of meaning. Paradoxical self-referential sentences can confuse our minds; they are like impossible figure illusions; they exist but are not understandable as a "whole", but interpretable as an "oscillation" of two contrasting level of meanings. Here are some everyday self-referential paradoxes:

– There are ALWAYS exceptions;
– You're unique like ALL of us;
– This species has ALWAYS been extinct;
– Superstition brings bad luck;
– I refuse to join a club in which they accept members like me;
– Is 'NO' your answer to this question?
– Expect the unexpected (Heraclitus);
– The two rules of success are: first, never divulge everything you know;
– Be spontaneous!
– Stop obeying me!

The writing in the sign means that the sign itself isn't a warning sign… But this is in contradiction to the word "caution". In the second example, how can someone who doesn't read English read the sentence 'if you cannot read English' on the label of the bottle?

Sure, not all self-referential sentences are paradoxical. Some are comparable to an "autistic" sentence which communicates with itself in loops (a sort of logical computer-type bug). The following short story illustrates the principle:

A Brief Reflection on Accuracy by Miroslav Holub (thanks to Professor Sergio Della Sala who brought this story to our attention)

A certain soldier had to fire a cannon at six o'clock sharp every evening. Being a soldier, he did so. When his accuracy was investigated he explained: 'I go by the absolutely accurate chronometer in the window of the clockmaker down in the city. Every day at 17.45 I set my watch by it and climb the hill where my cannon stands ready. At 17.59 precisely I step up to the cannon and at 18.00 sharp I fire'.

It was clear that this method of firing was absolutely accurate. All that was left was to check that chronometer. So the clockmaker down in the city was questioned about his instrument's accuracy. 'Oh, said the clockmaker, this is one of the most accurate instruments ever. Just imagine, for years now a cannon fires at six o'clock sharp every evening and my chronometer has always been bang on the hour…'

To conclude, here are some non-paradoxical self-referential sentences:

– This sentence finishes right here;
– Pentasyllabic (is a word of five syllables and means 'a word containing five syllables')
– This sentence was in the past tense;
– You may quote me.

The middle point

Which line (A, B or C) is positioned
exactly halfway up the spine of the book?

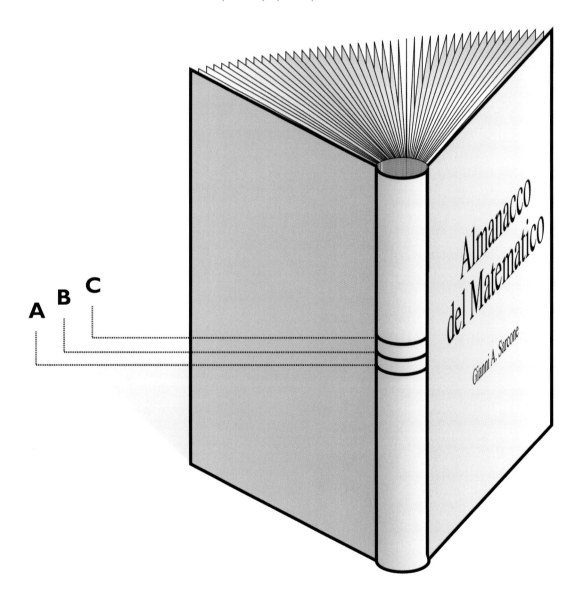

A B C

Almanacco
del Matematico

Gianni A. Sarcone

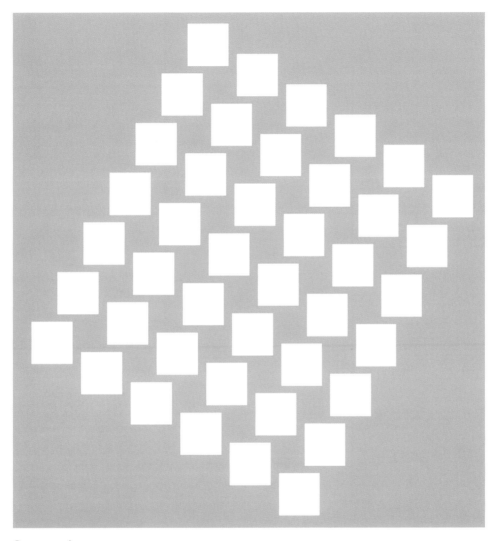

Squeezed squares
Are the white shapes perfect squares?
Do they have "pointed" corners?

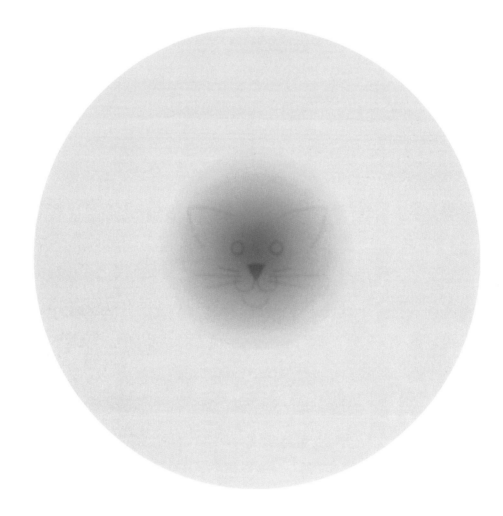

Cheshire Cat

Close one eye and focus your attention on the central blue haze to make the Cheshire Cat vanish. You'll notice that after approximately 15-20 seconds the blue haze gradually disappears along with the cat, but if you continue to stare, the cat will reappear...

90-degree angles

How many 90-degree angles are hidden in the picture?

Bowling ball illusion
Which ball is larger, the one which has been dropped by the player or the other one in the foreground?

Ladders
Do the ladders seem to wobble and bulge?

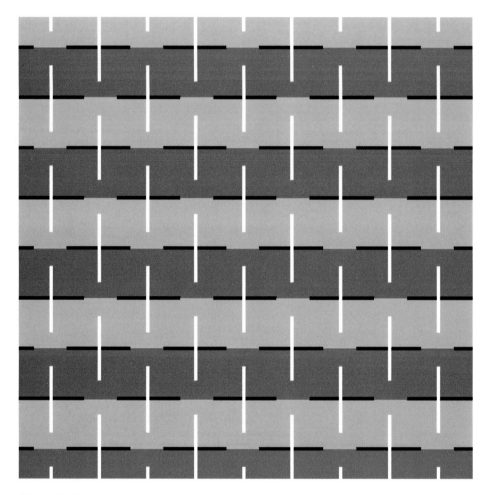

Xmas balls

Do you see illusory light bicolor discs in this pattern?

3D Grids

Do you see tridimensional grids? Is the red grid slightly distorted?

Glowing and scintillating

Shift your gaze around the picture. You may see ghost discs glowing at the intersection points of the bars while clear bright spots pop up in their middles.

Tilted frames
Are the squares skewed?

A

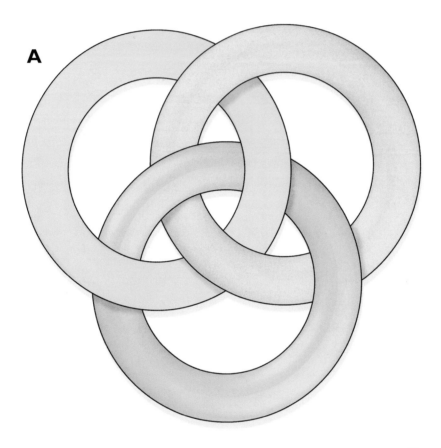

Borromean rings

Can three flat circles be interlinked as shown in A? Can you do the same with three paper clips?

B

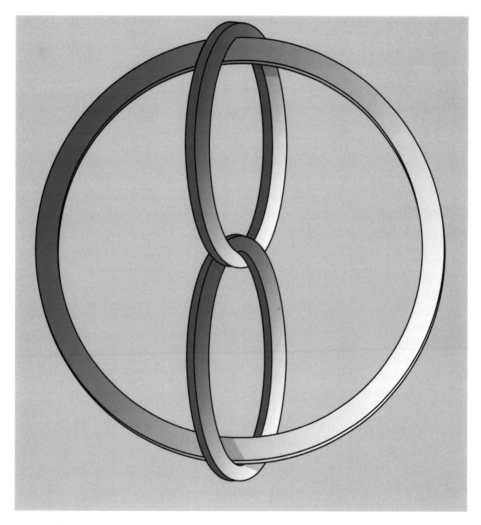

Impossible Borromean rings
An impossible 3D figure.

Gallery VI Notes

Page 144

Shape distortion can occur when contrasting objects are nearby. Yes, it's a perfect circle, though the points of the stars induce the circle to appear slightly flat. Actually, each set of four stars delimitates a square. Do you perceive them?

Page 145

As our tendency is to see vertical objects as slenderer than horizontal objects, the parallelogram shape which forms the horizontal axis of the cross appears larger than the parallelogram shape forming the vertical axis. So we perceive segment CD slightly larger than segment AB, despite the fact they are similar.

Page 146

The special asymmetric shape of the flakes is responsible for these illusions, but the lines are perfectly parallel. Here is an additional effect, if you shift your gaze around the flakes for a while, you may see a gray spot appear inside each flock.

Page 148

Line a; yes, sir.

Page 149

The shapes are perfect squares. Strangely enough, when perfect squares are assembled in regular sets, they tend to lose their regularity. The illusion works better when it is seen from a certain distance.

Page 150

Vision depends on the tiny imperceptible eye movements which keep the visual stimulus constant. In the picture, the gradual color difference from gray to blue is a poor stimulus for sustaining visual perception. However, if your eyes freely move over the stimulus the perception of it will be sustained. When you fixate the dark blue dot (the nose of the cat) and try holding your gaze as steady as possible, then the haze should fade away and the color of the background will predominate. The re-apparition of the cat will be triggered by a decisive eye movement.

Page 151

8! Generally people manage to locate up to 6 right angles relatively easy. A tough one to find is that on the upper side of the house in the background. Two or three 90-degree angles don't look very convincing, but this is entirely due to a trick of the apparent perspective.

Page 152

Both are the same size. This is a neat variant of the Ponzo illusion.

Page 153

The rungs of every second ladder are out of phase, causing this wobbling or bulging effect. This illusion is similar to the Café wall illusion.

Page 154

Light circular discs with phantom contours can be perceived over the empty spaces between the black and white lines. Scientists have proved that this kind of brightness illusion is not created in the retina, but as a consequence of interaction between both optic nerves in the higher regions of the brain cortex.

Both the phantom edge phenomenon shown in the picture (also called the Ehrenstein illusion) and the Kanisza figure illusion are triggered by the T-effect: there are groups of neural cells which react to line ends and without further input create the intersections to the horizontal bar of the letter T as a precautionary measure. Each intersection could indicate the concealment of a figure in the foreground, so recognition of a potential danger must be rapid. If various T elements indicate a distinct figure (eg. circle, square), the ghost contour is drawn in the head and the core of the figure is filled in with either the lightened or darkened background.

Page 155

No; obviously the grids are all located on the same plane. Brightness and color influence distance perception; bright, warm colors tend to be seen as closer than cold colors, creating a tridimensional effect.

Page 156

This illusion combines the Lingelbach grid effect with the Van Tuijl neon color illusion.

Page 157

No; they are perfectly aligned and parallel. Take a ruler and see for yourself! This is a kind of Zöllner illusion.

Page 158

If you try making the Borromean rings out of wire, you will find that you cannot make the figure with real flat circles. There must always be kinks. The theorem stating borromean rings to be

impossible with flat circles is proved in the article "Borromean circles are impossible" *American Mathematics Monthly*, 98 (1991), by B. Lindström and H-O. Zetterström.